Homework H

Subtraction Grade 3

As a parent, you want your child to enjoy learning and to do well in school. The activities in the *Homework Helpers* series will help your child develop the skills and self-confidence that lead to success. Humorous illustrations make these practice activities interesting for your child.

HOW TO USE THIS BOOK

- Provide a quiet, comfortable place to work with your child.

- Plan a special time to work with your child. Create a warm, accepting atmosphere so your child will enjoy spending this time with you. Limit each session to one or two activities.

- Check the answers with your child as soon as an activity has been completed. (Be sure to remove the answer pages from the center of the book before your child uses the book.)

- Topics covered in this book are subtraction facts, subtraction of one-, two-, three-, and four-digit numbers, subtraction with regrouping, and estimation.

- Each section includes one or two pages for reviewing the skills. Time these pages if your child has mastered the skill and is ready to work on improving speed.

Written by Sue Ryono
Illustrated by John Crum

SBN #0-86734-126-2

FS-8159 Homework Helpers—Subtraction Grade 3
All rights reserved—Printed in the U.S.A.
Copyright © 1992 Frank Schaffer Publications, Inc.
23740 Hawthorne Blvd., Torrance, CA 90505

This book or parts thereof may not be reproduced in any form or mechanically stored in any retrieval system without written permission from the publisher.

Homework Helper Record

Color the spot for each page
you complete.

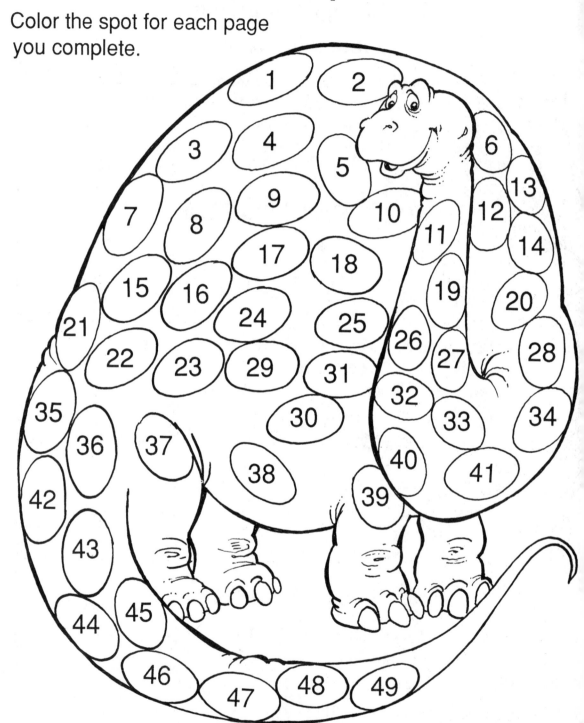

© Frank Schaffer Publications, Inc.

Warmup

A.

$$\begin{array}{r} 10 \\ -\ 1 \\ \hline \end{array} \qquad \begin{array}{r} 9 \\ -5 \\ \hline \end{array} \qquad \begin{array}{r} 8 \\ -7 \\ \hline \end{array} \qquad \begin{array}{r} 7 \\ -3 \\ \hline \end{array} \qquad \begin{array}{r} 10 \\ -\ 6 \\ \hline \end{array}$$

B.

$$\begin{array}{r} 7 \\ -4 \\ \hline \end{array} \qquad \begin{array}{r} 10 \\ -\ 2 \\ \hline \end{array} \qquad \begin{array}{r} 9 \\ -4 \\ \hline \end{array} \qquad \begin{array}{r} 10 \\ -\ 7 \\ \hline \end{array} \qquad \begin{array}{r} 8 \\ -6 \\ \hline \end{array}$$

C.

$$\begin{array}{r} 8 \\ -4 \\ \hline \end{array} \qquad \begin{array}{r} 9 \\ -6 \\ \hline \end{array} \qquad \begin{array}{r} 10 \\ -\ 3 \\ \hline \end{array} \qquad \begin{array}{r} 9 \\ -3 \\ \hline \end{array} \qquad \begin{array}{r} 8 \\ -5 \\ \hline \end{array}$$

D.

$$\begin{array}{r} 9 \\ -7 \\ \hline \end{array} \qquad \begin{array}{r} 10 \\ -\ 8 \\ \hline \end{array} \qquad \begin{array}{r} 8 \\ -3 \\ \hline \end{array} \qquad \begin{array}{r} 10 \\ -\ 4 \\ \hline \end{array} \qquad \begin{array}{r} 9 \\ -2 \\ \hline \end{array}$$

E.

$$\begin{array}{r} 10 \\ -\ 9 \\ \hline \end{array} \qquad \begin{array}{r} 8 \\ -2 \\ \hline \end{array} \qquad \begin{array}{r} 9 \\ -8 \\ \hline \end{array} \qquad \begin{array}{r} 9 \\ -9 \\ \hline \end{array} \qquad \begin{array}{r} 10 \\ -\ 5 \\ \hline \end{array}$$

F.

$$\begin{array}{r} 7 \\ -5 \\ \hline \end{array} \qquad \begin{array}{r} 7 \\ -2 \\ \hline \end{array} \qquad \begin{array}{r} 6 \\ -4 \\ \hline \end{array} \qquad \begin{array}{r} 7 \\ -6 \\ \hline \end{array} \qquad \begin{array}{r} 6 \\ -3 \\ \hline \end{array}$$

© Frank Schaffer Publications, Inc. FS-8159 Homework Helpers—Subtraction Grade 3

Review

A. $10 - 5 = $ _____ $9 - 5 = $ _____ $10 - 9 = $ _____

B. $9 - 6 = $ _____ $10 - 4 = $ _____ $9 - 7 = $ _____

C. $10 - 3 = $ _____ $10 - 2 = $ _____ $9 - 2 = $ _____

D. $9 - 3 = $ _____ $8 - 3 = $ _____ $10 - 6 = $ _____

E. $7 - 2 = $ _____ $10 - 7 = $ _____ $8 - 4 = $ _____

F. $10 - 0 = $ _____ $7 - 4 = $ _____ $10 - 8 = $ _____

G. $7 - 3 = $ _____ $9 - 8 = $ _____ $7 - 5 = $ _____

H. $7 - 6 = $ _____ $8 - 7 = $ _____ $9 - 4 = $ _____

I. $8 - 5 = $ _____ $6 - 2 = $ _____ $8 - 6 = $ _____

© Frank Schaffer Publications, Inc.   2

Small Change

Don't forget the cents sign.

A.

8¢	10¢	8¢	10¢	8¢
− 2¢	− 4¢	− 4¢	− 5¢	− 6¢
6¢				

B.

9¢	7¢	10¢	7¢	10¢
− 2¢	− 2¢	− 7¢	− 3¢	− 6¢

C.

10¢	8¢	7¢	8¢	10¢
− 8¢	− 8¢	− 4¢	− 3¢	− 2¢

D.

9¢	9¢	7¢	9¢	7¢
− 4¢	− 5¢	− 5¢	− 3¢	− 6¢

E.

8¢	9¢	10¢	8¢	10¢
− 5¢	− 7¢	− 3¢	− 7¢	− 9¢

F.

6¢	5¢	9¢	6¢	9¢
− 3¢	− 3¢	− 8¢	− 4¢	− 6¢

© Frank Schaffer Publications, Inc.

FS-8159 Homework Helpers—Subtraction Grade 3

Missing Numbers

Remember this?

A.
6 + 5 = ___
5 + 6 = ___
5 + ___ = 11
6 + ___ = 11
11 − 6 = ___
11 − 5 = ___

B.
4 + 7 = ___
7 + 4 = ___
7 + ___ = 11
4 + ___ = 11
11 − 7 = ___
11 − 4 = ___

C.
3 + 8 = ___
8 + 3 = ___
8 + ___ = 11
3 + ___ = 11
11 − 8 = ___
11 − 3 = ___

D.
5 + 7 = ___
7 + 5 = ___
7 + ___ = 12
5 + ___ = 12
12 − 7 = ___
12 − 5 = ___

E.
4 + 8 = ___
8 + 4 = ___
8 + ___ = 12
4 + ___ = 12
12 − 4 = ___
12 − 8 = ___

F.
3 + 9 = ___
9 + 3 = ___
9 + ___ = 12
3 + ___ = 12
12 − 9 = ___
12 − 3 = ___

Have Some Cents!

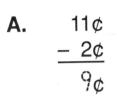

A.
$$\begin{array}{r} 11¢ \\ -\ 2¢ \\ \hline 9¢ \end{array}$$
$$\begin{array}{r} 12¢ \\ -\ 3¢ \\ \hline \end{array}$$
$$\begin{array}{r} 12¢ \\ -\ 7¢ \\ \hline \end{array}$$
$$\begin{array}{r} 11¢ \\ -\ 4¢ \\ \hline \end{array}$$

B.
$$\begin{array}{r} 12¢ \\ -\ 8¢ \\ \hline \end{array}$$
$$\begin{array}{r} 12¢ \\ -\ 6¢ \\ \hline \end{array}$$
$$\begin{array}{r} 11¢ \\ -\ 3¢ \\ \hline \end{array}$$
$$\begin{array}{r} 12¢ \\ -\ 5¢ \\ \hline \end{array}$$

C.
$$\begin{array}{r} 11¢ \\ -\ 5¢ \\ \hline \end{array}$$
$$\begin{array}{r} 12¢ \\ -\ 9¢ \\ \hline \end{array}$$
$$\begin{array}{r} 10¢ \\ -\ 2¢ \\ \hline \end{array}$$
$$\begin{array}{r} 11¢ \\ -\ 6¢ \\ \hline \end{array}$$

D.
$$\begin{array}{r} 10¢ \\ -\ 4¢ \\ \hline \end{array}$$
$$\begin{array}{r} 11¢ \\ -\ 8¢ \\ \hline \end{array}$$
$$\begin{array}{r} 10¢ \\ -\ 3¢ \\ \hline \end{array}$$
$$\begin{array}{r} 11¢ \\ -\ 7¢ \\ \hline \end{array}$$

E.
$$\begin{array}{r} 10¢ \\ -\ 5¢ \\ \hline \end{array}$$
$$\begin{array}{r} 10¢ \\ -\ 7¢ \\ \hline \end{array}$$
$$\begin{array}{r} 12¢ \\ -\ 4¢ \\ \hline \end{array}$$
$$\begin{array}{r} 10¢ \\ -\ 6¢ \\ \hline \end{array}$$

F.
$$\begin{array}{r} 11¢ \\ -\ 9¢ \\ \hline \end{array}$$
$$\begin{array}{r} 10¢ \\ -\ 9¢ \\ \hline \end{array}$$
$$\begin{array}{r} 11¢ \\ -\ 4¢ \\ \hline \end{array}$$
$$\begin{array}{r} 10¢ \\ -\ 8¢ \\ \hline \end{array}$$

Fill in the Boxes!

A.
$4 + 9 =$ ___
$9 + 4 =$ ___
$9 +$ ___ $= 13$
$4 +$ ___ $= 13$
$13 - 9 =$ ___
$13 - 4 =$ ___

B.
$5 + 8 =$ ___
$8 + 5 =$ ___
$8 +$ ___ $= 13$
$5 +$ ___ $= 13$
$13 - 8 =$ ___
$13 - 5 =$ ___

C.
$6 + 7 =$ ___
$7 + 6 =$ ___
$7 +$ ___ $= 13$
$6 +$ ___ $= 13$
$13 - 7 =$ ___
$13 - 6 =$ ___

D.
$5 + 9 =$ ___
$9 + 5 =$ ___
$9 +$ ___ $= 14$
$5 +$ ___ $= 14$
$14 - 9 =$ ___
$14 - 5 =$ ___

E.
$6 + 8 =$ ___
$8 + 6 =$ ___
$8 +$ ___ $= 14$
$6 +$ ___ $= 14$
$14 - 6 =$ ___
$14 - 8 =$ ___

F.
$7 + 7 =$ ___
$7 +$ ___ $= 14$
___ $+ 7 = 14$
$14 - 7 =$ ___

© Frank Schaffer Publications, Inc.

FS-8159 Homework Helpers—Subtraction Grade 3

Review

A. $11 - 2 =$ ___ $\quad\quad$ $12 - 4 =$ ___ $\quad\quad$ $12 - 3 =$ ___

B. $12 - 5 =$ ___ $\quad\quad$ $11 - 3 =$ ___ $\quad\quad$ $13 - 9 =$ ___

C. $11 - 5 =$ ___ $\quad\quad$ $13 - 8 =$ ___ $\quad\quad$ $11 - 4 =$ ___

D. $12 - 7 =$ ___ $\quad\quad$ $11 - 6 =$ ___ $\quad\quad$ $12 - 6 =$ ___

E. $11 - 8 =$ ___ $\quad\quad$ $13 - 7 =$ ___ $\quad\quad$ $11 - 7 =$ ___

F. $13 - 5 =$ ___ $\quad\quad$ $11 - 9 =$ ___ $\quad\quad$ $13 - 6 =$ ___

G. $12 - 8 =$ ___ $\quad\quad$ $13 - 4 =$ ___ $\quad\quad$ $12 - 9 =$ ___

H. $14 - 8 =$ ___ $\quad\quad$ $14 - 9 =$ ___

Score: _____

I. $14 - 7 =$ ___ $\quad\quad$ $14 - 6 =$ ___

Time: _____

© Frank Schaffer Publications, Inc. FS-8159 Homework Helpers—Subtraction Grade 3

A.

	11	12	11	13	13	14
	− 9	− 8	− 8	− 9	− 8	− 9

B.

	14	12	11	13	12	14
	− 8	− 9	− 7	− 7	− 7	− 7

C.

	11	12	11	11	13	14
	− 6	− 5	− 5	− 4	− 5	− 5

D.

	13	12	12	13	11	14
	− 4	− 6	− 4	− 8	− 9	− 8

E.

	13	11	13	14	12	12
	− 9	− 8	− 6	− 9	− 8	− 3

F.

	11	13	12	12
	− 7	− 7	− 7	− 4

Score: _____

Time: _____

Figure These Out!

A.
6 + 9 = ___

9 + 6 = ___

9 + ___ = 15

6 + ___ = 15

15 − 9 = ___

15 − 6 = ___

B.
7 + 8 = ___

8 + 7 = ___

8 + ___ = 15

7 + ___ = 15

15 − 8 = ___

15 − 7 = ___

C.
7 + 9 = ___

9 + 7 = ___

9 + ___ = 16

7 + ___ = 16

16 − 9 = ___

16 − 7 = ___

D.
8 + 9 = ___

9 + 8 = ___

9 + ___ = 17

8 + ___ = 17

17 − 9 = ___

17 − 8 = ___

E.
8 + 8 = ___

8 + ___ = 16

___ + 8 = 16

16 − 8 = ___

F.
9 + 9 = ___

9 + ___ = 18

___ + 9 = 18

18 − 9 = ___

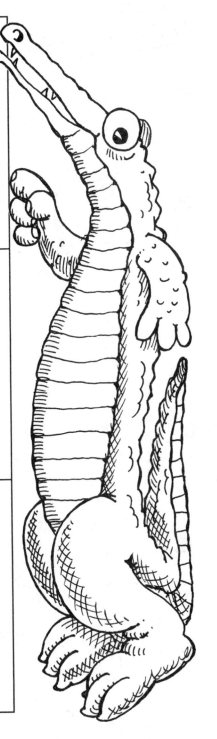

© Frank Schaffer Publications, Inc.   FS-8159 Homework Helpers—Subtraction Grade 3

Subtracting Cents

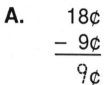

Don't forget to put a cent sign on your answer!

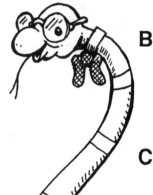

A.

18¢	16¢	17¢	16¢
− 9¢	− 8¢	− 9¢	− 9¢
9¢			

B.

15¢	15¢	16¢	17¢
− 9¢	− 7¢	− 7¢	− 8¢

C.

15¢	15¢	14¢	14¢
− 6¢	− 8¢	− 9¢	− 7¢

D.

14¢	14¢	13¢	13¢
− 8¢	− 6¢	− 4¢	− 6¢

E.

13¢	13¢	12¢	13¢
− 9¢	− 8¢	− 7¢	− 5¢

F.

13¢	12¢	12¢	12¢
− 7¢	− 9¢	− 5¢	− 8¢

Review

A. 16 − 9 = ___   17 − 9 = ___   16 − 7 = ___

B. 18 − 9 = ___   16 − 8 = ___   17 − 8 = ___

C. 14 − 7 = ___   14 − 9 = ___   15 − 6 = ___

D. 14 − 5 = ___   15 − 8 = ___   14 − 8 = ___

E. 15 − 9 = ___   14 − 6 = ___   15 − 7 = ___

F. 13 − 9 = ___   13 − 6 = ___   13 − 7 = ___

G. 12 − 8 = ___   13 − 8 = ___   13 − 5 = ___

H. 12 − 5 = ___   12 − 7 = ___

Score: _____

Time: _____

I. 12 − 6 = ___   13 − 4 = ___

© Frank Schaffer Publications, Inc.   11

Review

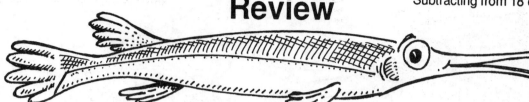

A.

16	13	14	14	16	1
− 9	− 9	− 7	− 5	− 7	−

B.

13	14	18	16	14	1
− 5	− 8	− 9	− 8	− 6	−

C.

14	12	13	12	17	1
− 9	− 9	− 7	− 7	− 9	−

D.

12	12	17	15	12	1
− 4	− 6	− 8	− 7	− 8	−

E.

11	15	12	12	11	1
− 9	− 8	− 5	− 3	− 7	−

F.

15	11	11	11
− 9	− 4	− 6	− 8

Score: _____

Time: _____

Subtract!

A.

56	94	83	72
− 42	− 50	− 63	− 40
14			

B.

65	46	38	92
− 35	− 23	− 17	− 31

C.

87	76	64	58
− 46	− 54	− 41	− 35

D.

95	84	67	98	86	97
− 23	− 12	− 25	− 36	− 45	− 50

E.

88	68	96	66	69	87
− 62	− 33	− 26	− 31	− 27	− 24

F.

57	47	49	54	85	48
− 32	− 23	− 15	− 23	− 34	− 24

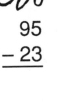

Money Again

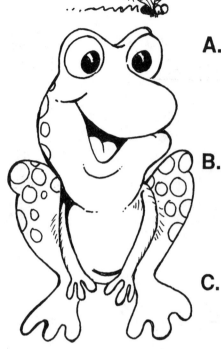

A.
$$29¢ - 4¢ = 25¢$$

$$38¢ - 12¢$$

$$53¢ - 30¢$$

$$78 - 26$$

B.
$$47¢ - 26¢$$

$$65¢ - 34¢$$

$$84¢ - 21¢$$

$$95 - 72$$

C.
$$21¢ - 11¢$$

$$36¢ - 22¢$$

$$55¢ - 22¢$$

$$64 - 2$$

D.
$$46¢ - 4¢$$

$$34¢ - 11¢$$

$$73¢ - 42¢$$

$$86¢ - 54¢$$

$$97¢ - 44¢$$

$$42 - 12$$

E.
$$58¢ - 6¢$$

$$69¢ - 7¢$$

$$76¢ - 23¢$$

$$88¢ - 54¢$$

$$94¢ - 32¢$$

$$35 - 23$$

F.
$$45¢ - 14¢$$

$$54¢ - 44¢$$

$$66¢ - 4¢$$

$$77¢ - 25¢$$

$$87¢ - 23¢$$

$$96 - 45$$

Nice Round Numbers

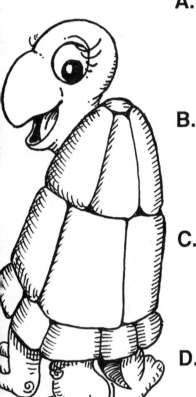

A.	40 − 20 20	90 − 30	80 − 60	50 − 20
B.	80 − 40	70 − 50	80 − 20	50 − 40
C.	90 − 50	70 − 20	80 − 50	90 − 40
D.	60 − 50	70 − 60	90 − 60	60 − 20

E.	90 − 70	70 − 30	90 − 20	70 − 40	50 − 30	80 − 30
F.	40 − 30	30 − 10	60 − 40	90 − 90	60 − 30	80 − 10

© Frank Schaffer Publications, Inc.   FS-8159 Homework Helpers—Subtraction Grade 3

Regrouping

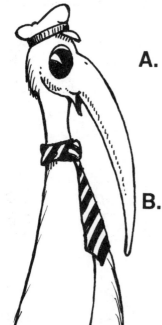

A.

$$\begin{array}{r} \overset{8}{\cancel{9}}^{1}4 \\ -26 \\ \hline 68 \end{array}$$

$$\begin{array}{r} 80 \\ -42 \\ \hline \end{array}$$

$$\begin{array}{r} 72 \\ -37 \\ \hline \end{array}$$

$$\begin{array}{r} 6\ \\ -4\ \\ \hline \end{array}$$

B.

$$\begin{array}{r} 63 \\ -27 \\ \hline \end{array}$$

$$\begin{array}{r} 74 \\ -18 \\ \hline \end{array}$$

$$\begin{array}{r} 93 \\ -35 \\ \hline \end{array}$$

$$\begin{array}{r} 5\ \\ -26 \\ \hline \end{array}$$

C.

$$\begin{array}{r} 51 \\ -17 \\ \hline \end{array}$$

$$\begin{array}{r} 73 \\ -48 \\ \hline \end{array}$$

$$\begin{array}{r} 82 \\ -38 \\ \hline \end{array}$$

$$\begin{array}{r} 64 \\ -28 \\ \hline \end{array}$$

D.

$$\begin{array}{r} 45 \\ -17 \\ \hline \end{array}$$

$$\begin{array}{r} 66 \\ -18 \\ \hline \end{array}$$

$$\begin{array}{r} 94 \\ -28 \\ \hline \end{array}$$

$$\begin{array}{r} 75 \\ -28 \\ \hline \end{array}$$

E.

$$\begin{array}{r} 83 \\ -36 \\ \hline \end{array}$$

$$\begin{array}{r} 42 \\ -19 \\ \hline \end{array}$$

$$\begin{array}{r} 31 \\ -14 \\ \hline \end{array}$$

$$\begin{array}{r} 50 \\ -22 \\ \hline \end{array}$$

Work Carefully!

A. $\begin{array}{r} 2\,5\,¢ \\ -\ 6\,¢ \\ \hline 1\,9\,¢ \end{array}$ $\begin{array}{r} 2\,8\,¢ \\ -\ 9\,¢ \\ \hline \end{array}$ $\begin{array}{r} 3\,6\,¢ \\ -1\,8\,¢ \\ \hline \end{array}$ $\begin{array}{r} 5\,0\,¢ \\ -2\,0\,¢ \\ \hline \end{array}$

B. $\begin{array}{r} 8\,5\,¢ \\ -7\,2\,¢ \\ \hline \end{array}$ $\begin{array}{r} 7\,1\,¢ \\ -\ 6\,¢ \\ \hline \end{array}$ $\begin{array}{r} 4\,5\,¢ \\ -1\,8\,¢ \\ \hline \end{array}$ $\begin{array}{r} 7\,6\,¢ \\ -\ 9\,¢ \\ \hline \end{array}$

C. $\begin{array}{r} 7\,3\,¢ \\ -\ 7\,¢ \\ \hline \end{array}$ $\begin{array}{r} 6\,1\,¢ \\ -5\,0\,¢ \\ \hline \end{array}$ $\begin{array}{r} 7\,2\,¢ \\ -2\,4\,¢ \\ \hline \end{array}$ $\begin{array}{r} 8\,0\,¢ \\ -3\,0\,¢ \\ \hline \end{array}$ $\begin{array}{r} 8\,8\,¢ \\ -2\,5\,¢ \\ \hline \end{array}$ $\begin{array}{r} 8\,4\,¢ \\ -\ 7\,¢ \\ \hline \end{array}$

D. $\begin{array}{r} 7\,5\,¢ \\ -2\,5\,¢ \\ \hline \end{array}$ $\begin{array}{r} 9\,0\,¢ \\ -4\,0\,¢ \\ \hline \end{array}$ $\begin{array}{r} 8\,7\,¢ \\ -3\,8\,¢ \\ \hline \end{array}$ $\begin{array}{r} 7\,4\,¢ \\ -3\,6\,¢ \\ \hline \end{array}$ $\begin{array}{r} 3\,0\,¢ \\ -\ 6\,¢ \\ \hline \end{array}$ $\begin{array}{r} 8\,3\,¢ \\ -5\,1\,¢ \\ \hline \end{array}$

E. $\begin{array}{r} 8\,2\,¢ \\ -2\,7\,¢ \\ \hline \end{array}$ $\begin{array}{r} 6\,3\,¢ \\ -2\,6\,¢ \\ \hline \end{array}$ $\begin{array}{r} 6\,2\,¢ \\ -2\,7\,¢ \\ \hline \end{array}$ $\begin{array}{r} 8\,6\,¢ \\ -4\,9\,¢ \\ \hline \end{array}$ $\begin{array}{r} 6\,4\,¢ \\ -2\,5\,¢ \\ \hline \end{array}$ $\begin{array}{r} 7\,0\,¢ \\ -5\,0\,¢ \\ \hline \end{array}$

Find a Pattern!

A.		B.	
16 − 10	16 − 9	14 − 10	14 − 9
C.		**D.**	
23 − 10	23 − 9	46 − 10	46 − 9

E.   13   27   35   58   92   6
       − 10   − 10   − 10   − 10   − 10   − 1

F.   15   54   31   65   42   7
       − 9   − 9   − 9   − 9   − 9   −

G.   87   26   98   35   67   8
       − 9   − 9   − 9   − 9   − 9   −

Rewrite and Solve!

Line up the columns!

A. $48 - 19 = \underline{\ ?\ }$ $\overset{3}{\cancel{4}}{}^{1}8$ $-\ 19$ ─── $2\ 9$	**B.** $56 - 28 = \underline{\ ?\ }$
C. $94 - 35 = \underline{\ ?\ }$	**D.** $82 - 45 = \underline{\ ?\ }$ **E.** $71 - 7 = \underline{\ ?\ }$
F. $63 - 17 = \underline{\ ?\ }$	**G.** $85 - 8 = \underline{\ ?\ }$ **H.** $93 - 35 = \underline{\ ?\ }$
I. $34 - 27 = \underline{\ ?\ }$	**J.** $76 - 28 = \underline{\ ?\ }$ **K.** $53 - 39 = \underline{\ ?\ }$

Estimate the Answer!

Put an X by the best answer.

A. 49 − 18 = ?

○ about 10
⊗ about 30
○ about 50
○ about 70

B. 91 − 52 = ?

○ about 20
○ about 40
○ about 60
○ about 80

C. 75 − 25 = ?

○ about 10
○ about 30
○ about 50
○ about 70

D. 60 − 19 = ?

○ about 20
○ about 40
○ about 60
○ about 80

E. 89 − 10 = ?

○ about 20
○ about 40
○ about 60
○ about 80

F. 61 − 22 = ?

○ about 20
○ about 40
○ about 60
○ about 80

G. 52 − 31 = ?

○ about 20
○ about 40
○ about 60
○ about 80

H. 49 − 21 = ?

○ about 10
○ about 30
○ about 50
○ about 70

I. 86 − 72 = ?

○ about 20
○ about 40
○ about 60
○ about 80

J. 93 − 28 = ?

○ about 20
○ about 40
○ about 60
○ about 80

K. 58 − 12 = ?

○ about 10
○ about 30
○ about 50
○ about 70

Bigger Numbers

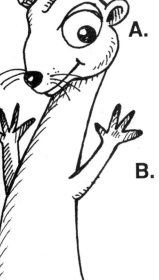

A.
$$847 - 223 = 624$$
$$956 - 622$$
$$747 - 413$$
$$658 - 16$$

B.
$$594 - 2$$
$$498 - 176$$
$$367 - 101$$
$$487 - 200$$

C.
$$586 - 423$$
$$642 - 21$$
$$793 - 101$$
$$937 - 700$$

D.
$$859 - 327$$
$$720 - 510$$
$$635 - 135$$
$$540 - 420$$

E.
$$456 - 356$$
$$475 - 242$$
$$567 - 135$$
$$666 - 15$$

© Frank Schaffer Publications, Inc.

FS-8159 Homework Helpers—Subtraction Grade 3

Round Numbers

A.
900	700	800	90
− 300	− 500	− 300	− 60
600			

B.
700	900	600	80
− 200	− 400	− 400	− 20

C.
600	800	900	80
− 100	− 500	− 400	− 40

D.
800	900	700	90
− 600	− 500	− 400	− 70

E.
600	900	600	700
− 300	− 200	− 200	− 300

More Money

A.
$9.55	$8.27	$7.45
− 7.21	− 1.25	− 3.45

B.
$6.54	$5.78	$4.95
− 2.50	− 2.70	− 1.01

C.
$5.96	$8.00	$6.79
− 2.96	− 5.00	− 2.57

D.
$7.00	$7.85	$5.45
− 2.00	− 3.64	− 2.00

E.
$4.69	$9.36	$8.99
− 2.24	− 2.03	− 5.26

More Regrouping

A.
$$
\begin{array}{r}
8\,\overset{4}{\cancel{5}}\,0 \\
-1\,2\,5 \\
\hline
7\,2\,5
\end{array}
$$

$$
\begin{array}{r}
9\,4\,2 \\
-4\,2\,6 \\
\hline
\end{array}
$$

$$
\begin{array}{r}
7\,9 \\
-1\,3 \\
\hline
\end{array}
$$

B.
$$
\begin{array}{r}
6\,4\,0 \\
-\ \ \ \,6 \\
\hline
\end{array}
$$

$$
\begin{array}{r}
5\,5\,1 \\
-\ \,3\,7 \\
\hline
\end{array}
$$

$$
\begin{array}{r}
4\,6 \\
-2\,1 \\
\hline
\end{array}
$$

C.
$$
\begin{array}{r}
5\,8\,2 \\
-\ \,4\,9 \\
\hline
\end{array}
$$

$$
\begin{array}{r}
6\,8\,4 \\
-6\,0\,6 \\
\hline
\end{array}
$$

$$
\begin{array}{r}
7\,9 \\
-\ \,8 \\
\hline
\end{array}
$$

D.
$$
\begin{array}{r}
8\,8\,4 \\
-4\,2\,6 \\
\hline
\end{array}
$$

$$
\begin{array}{r}
9\,7\,3 \\
-3\,2\,6 \\
\hline
\end{array}
$$

$$
\begin{array}{r}
8\,6 \\
-\ \,4 \\
\hline
\end{array}
$$

E.
$$
\begin{array}{r}
7\,5\,1 \\
-2\,3\,2 \\
\hline
\end{array}
$$

$$
\begin{array}{r}
6\,4\,0 \\
-3\,2\,7 \\
\hline
\end{array}
$$

$$
\begin{array}{r}
5\,5 \\
-2\,2\,8 \\
\hline
\end{array}
$$

© Frank Schaffer Publications, Inc.

Pull-Out Answers

Page 1
A. 9, 4, 1, 4, 4
B. 3, 8, 5, 3, 2
C. 4, 3, 7, 6, 3
D. 2, 2, 5, 6, 7
E. 1, 6, 1, 0, 5
F. 2, 5, 2, 1, 3

Page 2
A. 5, 4, 1
B. 3, 6, 2
C. 7, 8, 7
D. 6, 5, 4
E. 5, 3, 4
F. 10, 3, 2
G. 4, 1, 2
H. 1, 1, 5
I. 3, 4, 2

Page 3
A. 6¢, 6¢, 4¢, 5¢, 2¢
B. 7¢, 5¢, 3¢, 4¢, 4¢
C. 2¢, 0¢, 3¢, 5¢, 8¢
D. 5¢, 4¢, 2¢, 6¢, 1¢
E. 3¢, 2¢, 7¢, 1¢, 1¢
F. 3¢, 2¢, 1¢, 2¢, 3¢

Page 4
A. 11, 11, 6, 5, 5, 6
B. 11, 11, 4, 7, 4, 7
C. 11, 11, 3, 8, 3, 8
D. 12, 12, 5, 7, 5, 7
E. 12, 12, 4, 8, 8, 4
F. 12, 12, 3, 9, 3, 9

Page 5
A. 9¢, 9¢, 5¢, 7¢
B. 4¢, 6¢, 8¢, 7¢
C. 6¢, 3¢, 8¢, 5¢
D. 6¢, 3¢, 7¢, 4¢
E. 5¢, 3¢, 8¢, 4¢
F. 2¢, 1¢, 7¢, 2¢

Page 6
A. 13, 13, 4, 9, 4, 9
B. 13, 13, 5, 8, 5, 8
C. 13, 13, 6, 7, 6, 7
D. 14, 14, 5, 9, 5, 9
E. 14, 14, 6, 8, 8, 6
F. 14, 7, 7, 7

Page 7
A. 9, 8, 9
B. 7, 8, 4
C. 6, 5, 7
D. 5, 5, 6
E. 3, 6, 4
F. 8, 2, 7
G. 4, 9, 3
H. 6, 5
I. 7, 8

Page 8
A. 2, 4, 3, 4, 5, 5
B. 6, 3, 4, 6, 5, 7
C. 5, 7, 6, 7, 8, 9
D. 9, 6, 8, 5, 2, 6
E. 4, 3, 7, 5, 4, 9
F. 4, 6, 5, 8

Page 9
A. 15, 15, 6, 9, 6, 9
B. 15, 15, 7, 8, 7, 8
C. 16, 16, 7, 9, 7, 9
D. 17, 17, 8, 9, 8, 9
E. 16, 8, 8, 8
F. 18, 9, 9, 9

Page 10
A. 9¢, 8¢, 8¢, 7¢
B. 6¢, 8¢, 9¢, 9¢
C. 9¢, 7¢, 5¢, 7¢
D. 6¢, 8¢, 9¢, 7¢
E. 4¢, 5¢, 5¢, 8¢
F. 6¢, 3¢, 7¢, 4¢

Page 11
A. 7, 8, 9
B. 9, 8, 9
C. 7, 5, 9
D. 9, 7, 6
E. 6, 8, 8
F. 4, 7, 6
G. 4, 5, 8
H. 7, 5
I. 6, 9

Page 12
A. 7, 4, 7, 9, 9, 5
B. 8, 6, 9, 8, 8, 7
C. 5, 3, 6, 5, 8, 9
D. 8, 6, 9, 8, 4, 9
E. 2, 7, 7, 9, 4, 6
F. 6, 7, 5, 3

Page 13
A. 14, 44, 20, 32
B. 30, 23, 21, 61
C. 41, 22, 23, 23
D. 72, 72, 42, 62, 41, 47
E. 26, 35, 70, 35, 42, 63
F. 25, 24, 34, 31, 51, 24

Page 14
A. 25¢, 26¢, 23¢, 52¢
B. 21¢, 31¢, 63¢, 23¢
C. 10¢, 14¢, 33¢, 62¢
D. 42¢, 23¢, 31¢, 32¢, 53¢, 30¢
E. 52¢, 62¢, 53¢, 34¢, 62¢, 12¢
F. 31¢, 10¢, 62¢, 52¢, 64¢, 51¢

Page 15
A. 20, 60, 20, 30
B. 40, 20, 60, 10
C. 40, 50, 30, 50
D. 10, 10, 30, 40
E. 20, 40, 70, 30, 20, 50
F. 10, 20, 20, 0, 30, 70

© Frank Schaffer Publications, Inc.

Pull-Out Answers

Page 16
A. 68, 38, 35, 15
B. 36, 56, 58, 26
C. 34, 25, 44, 36
D. 28, 48, 66, 47
E. 47, 23, 17, 28

Page 17
A. 19¢, 19¢, 18¢, 30¢
B. 13¢, 65¢, 27¢, 67¢
C. 66¢, 11¢, 48¢, 50¢, 63¢, 77¢
D. 50¢, 50¢, 49¢, 38¢, 24¢, 32¢
E. 55¢, 37¢, 35¢, 37¢, 39¢, 20¢

Page 18
A. 6, 7
B. 4, 5
C. 13, 14
D. 36, 37
E. 3, 17, 25, 48, 82, 54
F. 6, 45, 22, 56, 33, 64
G. 78, 17, 89, 26, 58, 73

Page 19
A. 29
B. 28
C. 59
D. 37
E. 64
F. 46
G. 77
H. 58
I. 7
J. 48
K. 14

Page 20
A. about 30
B. about 40
C. about 50
D. about 40
E. about 80
F. about 40
G. about 20
H. about 30
I. about 20
J. about 60
K. about 50

Page 21
A. 624, 334, 334, 642
B. 592, 322, 266, 287
C. 163, 621, 692, 237
D. 532, 210, 500, 120
E. 100, 233, 432, 651

Page 22
A. 600, 200, 500, 300
B. 500, 500, 200, 600
C. 500, 300, 500, 400
D. 200, 400, 300, 200
E. 300, 700, 400, 400

Page 23
A. $2.34, $7.02, $4.00
B. ¢4.04, $3.08, $3.94
C. $3.00, $3.00, $4.22
D. $5.00, $4.21, $3.45
E. $2.45, $7.33, $3.73

Page 24
A. 725, 516, 657
B. 634, 514, 247
C. 533, 78, 709
D. 458, 647, 814
E. 519, 313, 323

Page 25
A. 544, 635, 518
B. 516, 176, 115
C. 236, 190, 372
D. 539, 482, 241, 157
E. 336, 205, 383, 419

Page 26
A. 806, 616, 466
B. 544, 548, 297
C. 424, 580, 695
D. 574, 217, 444
E. 469, 488, 430

Page 27
A. $7.28, $2.95, $2.50
B. $3.92, $2.12, $2.33
C. $2.16, $3.91, $2.77, $6.70
D. $3.85, $4.52, $4.84, $2.92
E. $3.42, $4.14, $1.86, $7.32

Page 28
A. 295, 295, 545, 356
B. 366, 373, 365, 343
C. 658, 147, 215, 127

Page 29
A. 766, 396, 325, 247
B. 154, 636, 88, 4
C. 300, 541, 257, 393
D. 73, 7, 581

© Frank Schaffer Publications, Inc.

B

Pull-Out Answers

Page 30
A. 319
B. 225
C. 474
D. 718
E. 798
F. 483
G. 549
H. 475
I. 181
J. 427
K. 135

Page 31
A. about 400
B. about 300
C. about 800
D. about 300
E. about 400
F. about 300
G. about 500
H. about 600
I. about 500
J. about 100
K. about 600

Page 32
A. about $4.00
B. about $7.00
C. about $5.00
D. about $7.00
E. about $6.00
F. about $2.00
G. about $6.00
H. about $8.00
I. about $2.00
J. about $6.00
K. about $8.00

Page 33
A. 3,223; 2,333; 5,217
B. 5,276; 5,162; 2,533
C. 2,545; 4,532; 2,506
D. 4,213; 6,641; 3,162
E. 4,233; 6,013; 1,273

Page 34
A. $25.49, $23.30, $43.40
B. $55.52, $61.10, $62.24
C. $52.56, $20.14, $33.35
D. $25.14, $22.32, $42.72
E. $72.27, $11.11, $21.52

Page 35
A. 6,000; 2,000; 6,000
B. 4,000; 3,000; 4,000
C. 5,000; 3,000; 2,000
D. 5,000; 2,000; 3,000
E. 7,000; 0; 5,000

Page 36
A. $20.00, $70.00, $30.00, $50.00
B. $50.00, $40.00, $30.00, $20.00
C. $30.00, $60.00, $50.00, $25.00
D. $10.00, $60.00, $20.00, $70.00

Page 37
A. 2,503; 3,208; 4,128
B. 1,140; 1,417; 4,457
C. 4,735; 4,108; 5,442
D. 2,425; 3,218; 2,338

Page 38
A. 4,843; 3,919; 3,144
B. 3,182; 5,819; 5,270
C. 4,059; 4,163; 2,815
D. 2,953; 1,809; 611

Page 39
A. 3,874; 4,459; 4,802
B. 5,099; 3,497; 2,344
C. 3,429; 3,094; 4,990
D. 3,624; 2,787; 3,101

Page 40
A. $19.51, $35.50, $23.25
B. $15.17, $14.90, $53.51
C. $22.11, $23.10, $27.56
D. $40.71, $25.21, $52.29

Page 41
A. 3,295; 1,882; 4,852
B. 5,580; 6,267; 3,571
C. 3,269; 3,278; 7,256
D. 3,759; 4,157; 1,768

Page 42
A. 6,877; 4,436; 2,678; 2,759
B. 2,398; 4,595; 3,371; 3,649
C. 3,773; 1,779; 4,996; 5,889

Page 43
A. 3,222; 2,667; 1,795; 3,969
B. 5,188; 4,079; 4,991; 6,240
C. 4,994; 2,998
D. 3,279; 2,889

Page 44
A. $9.93, $20.05, $52.50
B. $17.98, $26.25, $40.10
C. $49.97, $52.41, $79.23
D. $36.01, $17.91, $22.02

Page 45
A. 4,819; 4,069; 3,127; 8,995
B. 6,673; 3,798; 1,888; 3,101
C. 886; 6,778; 4,906
D. 2,088; 2,780; 1,993

Pull Out Answers

Page 46
A. 2,122
B. 4,405
C. 8,820
D. 8,992
E. 7,834
F. 8,321
G. 7,333
H. 6,943
I. 5,245
J. 4,068
K. 7,267

Page 47
A. about 5,000
B. about 3,000
C. about 6,000
D. about 2,000
E. about 1,000
F. about 4,000
G. about 5,000
H. about 1,000
I. about 7,000
J. about 3,000
K. about 2,000

Page 48
A. about $45.00
B. about $15.00
C. about $30.00
D. about $30.00
E. about $50.00
F. about $60.00
G. about $60.00
H. about $30.00
I. about $55.00
J. about $40.00
K. about $5.00
L. about $25.00

Page 49
A. 9,397; 6,571, 657; 4,151
B. 5,001; 4,000; 4,092;
    4,195
C. 7,644; 4,026; 5,999

© Frank Schaffer Publications, Inc.

D

Practice

Is this
one
correct?

A.
$$5\overset{5}{\cancel{6}}3$$
$$-\ \ 19$$
$$\overline{5\ 4\ 4}$$

928
−293

865
−347

B.
741
−225

637
−461

542
−427

C.
492
−256

385
−195

465
− 93

D.
588
− 49

642
−160

723
−482

807
−650

E.
945
−609

520
−315

808
−425

946
−527

© Frank Schaffer Publications, Inc.

Concentrate!

We'll help.

A.

$$9\overset{4}{\cancel{9}}5$$
$$-149$$
$$\overline{806}$$

$$832$$
$$-216$$

$$721$$
$$-255$$

B.

$$643$$
$$-\ 99$$

$$594$$
$$-\ 46$$

$$421$$
$$-124$$

C.

$$533$$
$$-109$$

$$620$$
$$-\ 40$$

$$720$$
$$-\ 25$$

D.

$$832$$
$$-258$$

$$920$$
$$-703$$

$$872$$
$$-428$$

E.

$$763$$
$$-294$$

$$654$$
$$-166$$

$$526$$
$$-\ 96$$

Dollars and Cents

A.

$9.47
− 2.19

$8.20
− 5.25

$7.00
− 4.50

B.

$5.90
− 1.98

$4.87
− 2.75

$5.32
− 2.99

C.

$6.61
− 4.45

$7.54
− 3.63

$8.65
− 5.88

$9.20
− 2.50

D.

$8.34
− 4.49

$7.88
− 3.36

$8.20
− 3.36

$9.41
− 6.49

E.

$6.36
− 2.94

$5.42
− 1.28

$7.74
− 5.88

$9.67
− 2.35

Pay Attention!

A.

$$\begin{array}{r} 804 \\ -509 \\ \hline \end{array}$$

$$\begin{array}{r} 703 \\ -408 \\ \hline \end{array}$$

$$\begin{array}{r} 902 \\ -357 \\ \hline \end{array}$$

$$\begin{array}{r} 601 \\ -245 \\ \hline \end{array}$$

B.

$$\begin{array}{r} 502 \\ -136 \\ \hline \end{array}$$

$$\begin{array}{r} 600 \\ -227 \\ \hline \end{array}$$

$$\begin{array}{r} 703 \\ -338 \\ \hline \end{array}$$

$$\begin{array}{r} 802 \\ -459 \\ \hline \end{array}$$

C.

$$\begin{array}{r} 907 \\ -249 \\ \hline \end{array}$$

$$\begin{array}{r} 503 \\ -356 \\ \hline \end{array}$$

$$\begin{array}{r} 402 \\ -187 \\ \hline \end{array}$$

$$\begin{array}{r} 304 \\ -177 \\ \hline \end{array}$$

Review

A.

```
  865        400        553        402
-  99       -   4      -228       -155
```

B.

```
  643        905        537        653
 -489       -269       -449       -649
```

C.

```
  700        835        756        700
 -400       -294       -499       -307
```

D.

```
  562        732        600
 -489       -725       -  19
```

Score: _____

Time: _____

Rewrite and Solve!

Line up the columns!

A. $545 - 226 = ?$ $$\begin{array}{r} 5\overset{3}{\cancel{4}}5 \\ -226 \\ \hline 319 \end{array}$$	**B.** $650 - 425 = ?$
C. $723 - 249 = ?$	**D.** $800 - 82 = ?$ **E.** $907 - 109 = ?$
F. $832 - 349 = ?$	**G.** $708 - 159 = ?$ **H.** $600 - 125 = ?$
I. $328 - 147 = ?$	**J.** $852 - 425 = ?$ **K.** $521 - 386 = ?$

Just Estimate

A. 500 − 97 = ?

○ about 200
⊗ about 400
○ about 600
○ about 800

B. 470 − 160 = ?

○ about 100
○ about 300
○ about 500
○ about 700

C. 903 − 100 = ?

○ about 200
○ about 400
○ about 600
○ about 800

D. 499 − 200 = ?

○ about 100
○ about 300
○ about 500
○ about 700

E. 765 − 365 = ?

○ about 200
○ about 400
○ about 600
○ about 800

F. 506 − 204 = ?

○ about 100
○ about 300
○ about 500
○ about 700

G. 698 − 201 = ?

○ about 100
○ about 300
○ about 500
○ about 700

H. 897 − 299 = ?

○ about 200
○ about 400
○ about 600
○ about 800

I. 664 − 230 = ?

○ about 100
○ about 300
○ about 500
○ about 700

J. 795 − 720 = ?

○ about 100
○ about 300
○ about 500
○ about 700

K. 807 − 198 = ?

○ about 200
○ about 400
○ about 600
○ about 800

© Frank Schaffer Publications, Inc.
FS-8159 Homework Helpers—Subtraction Grade 3

Select the Best Answer!

A. $9.05 − $5.00 =?
- ○ about $2.00
- ⊗ about $4.00
- ○ about $6.00
- ○ about $8.00

B. $7.99 − $1.00 =?
- ○ about $1.00
- ○ about $3.00
- ○ about $5.00
- ○ about $7.00

C. $7.55 − $2.50 =?
- ○ about $1.00
- ○ about $3.00
- ○ about $5.00
- ○ about $7.00

D. $9.03 − $2.00 =?
- ○ about $1.00
- ○ about $3.00
- ○ about $5.00
- ○ about $7.00

E. $8.52 − $2.50 =?
- ○ about $2.00
- ○ about $4.00
- ○ about $6.00
- ○ about $8.00

F. $8.03 − $6.00 =?
- ○ about $2.00
- ○ about $4.00
- ○ about $6.00
- ○ about $8.00

G. $7.01 − $1.00 =?
- ○ about $2.00
- ○ about $4.00
- ○ about $6.00
- ○ about $8.00

H. $9.05 − $1.40 =?
- ○ about $2.00
- ○ about $4.00
- ○ about $6.00
- ○ about $8.00

I. $6.59 − $5.06 =?
- ○ about $2.00
- ○ about $4.00
- ○ about $6.00
- ○ about $8.00

J. $9.10 − $2.99 =?
- ○ about $2.00
- ○ about $4.00
- ○ about $6.00
- ○ about $8.00

K. $9.75 − $2.29 =?
- ○ about $2.00
- ○ about $4.00
- ○ about $6.00
- ○ about $8.00

Even Bigger Numbers!

I guess I can't do these on my fingers.

A.
$$5,429 - 2,206$$ $$6,983 - 4,650$$ $$9,729 - 4,512$$

B.
$$8,576 - 3,300$$ $$7,564 - 2,402$$ $$4,858 - 2,325$$

C.
$$5,977 - 3,432$$ $$6,777 - 2,245$$ $$7,829 - 5,323$$

D.
$$8,794 - 4,581$$ $$9,863 - 3,222$$ $$8,599 - 5,437$$

E.
$$6,548 - 2,315$$ $$7,075 - 1,062$$ $$3,897 - 2,624$$

What's Left?

A. $49.99 $65.49 $78.69
     - 24.50   - 42.19   - 35.29
     $25.49

B. $85.75 $97.50 $83.78
     - 30.23   - 36.40   - 21.54

C. $75.57 $60.39 $57.85
     - 23.01   - 40.25   - 24.50

D. $48.79 $37.88 $77.98
     - 23.65   - 15.56   - 35.26

E. $95.68 $48.84 $66.73
     - 23.41   - 37.73   - 45.21

Quick Calculations

I can zip through this page!

A.
$$8,000 - 2,000$$
$$7,000 - 5,000$$
$$9,000 - 3,000$$

B.
$$9,000 - 5,000$$
$$8,000 - 5,000$$
$$7,000 - 3,000$$

C.
$$8,000 - 3,000$$
$$9,000 - 6,000$$
$$6,000 - 4,000$$

D.
$$7,000 - 2,000$$
$$9,000 - 7,000$$
$$7,000 - 4,000$$

E.
$$9,000 - 2,000$$
$$8,000 - 8,000$$
$$9,000 - 4,000$$

Money Math

A.
$65.00
− 45.00

$90.00
− 20.00

$65.00
− 35.00

$90.00
− 40.00

B.
$70.00
− 20.00

$50.00
− 10.00

$70.00
− 40.00

$45.00
− 25.00

C.
$80.00
− 50.00

$90.00
− 30.00

$75.00
− 25.00

$35.00
− 10.00

D.
$35.00
− 25.00

$80.00
− 20.00

$50.00
− 30.00

$85.00
− 15.00

Try These!

A. 7,522   8,436   9,275
      −5,019   −5,228   −5,147
      ‾‾‾‾‾
       2,503

B. 6,249   5,426   6,580
      −5,109   −4,009   −2,123

C. 7,950   8,210   9,564
      −3,215   −4,102   −4,122

D. 6,770   5,375   4,781
      −4,345   −2,157   −2,443

© Frank Schaffer Publications, Inc.   37   FS-8159 Homework Helpers—Subtraction Grade 3

More Regrouping!

Tricky!

A.
$$\begin{array}{r} \overset{8}{\cancel{9}},4\overset{5}{\cancel{6}}\,{}^1\!2 \\ -\,4,619 \\ \hline 4,843 \end{array}$$

$$\begin{array}{r} 8,096 \\ -\,4,177 \\ \hline \end{array}$$

$$\begin{array}{r} 7,323 \\ -\,4,179 \\ \hline \end{array}$$

B.
$$\begin{array}{r} 6,357 \\ -\,3,175 \\ \hline \end{array}$$

$$\begin{array}{r} 9,290 \\ -\,3,471 \\ \hline \end{array}$$

$$\begin{array}{r} 8,842 \\ -\,3,572 \\ \hline \end{array}$$

C.
$$\begin{array}{r} 7,983 \\ -\,3,924 \\ \hline \end{array}$$

$$\begin{array}{r} 6,438 \\ -\,2,275 \\ \hline \end{array}$$

$$\begin{array}{r} 5,621 \\ -\,2,806 \\ \hline \end{array}$$

D.
$$\begin{array}{r} 4,760 \\ -\,1,807 \\ \hline \end{array}$$

$$\begin{array}{r} 3,527 \\ -\,1,718 \\ \hline \end{array}$$

$$\begin{array}{r} 2,130 \\ -\,1,519 \\ \hline \end{array}$$

© Frank Schaffer Publications, Inc.

FS-8159 Homework Helpers—Subtraction Grade 3

Time to Think

Wow!

A.　9,520　　　8,435　　　7,231
　　　−5,646　　−3,976　　−2,429

B.　6,420　　　5,632　　　4,590
　　　−1,321　　−2,135　　−2,246

C.　5,240　　　6,871　　　7,429
　　　−1,811　　−3,777　　−2,439

D.　8,273　　　9,135　　　8,710
　　　−4,649　　−6,348　　−5,609

More Money

A. $49.50 $75.00 $63.20
       – 29.99   – 39.50   – 39.95

B. $85.12 $52.50 $91.10
       – 69.95   – 37.60   – 37.59

C. $87.40 $73.20 $64.35
       – 65.29   – 50.10   – 36.79

D. $53.40 $43.20 $72.24
       – 12.69   – 17.99   – 19.95

Working With Zeros

I may
need help.

A.   8,304   9,200   7,025
       −5,009   −7,318   −2,173

B.   8,040   9,602   6,013
       −2,460   −3,335   −2,442

C.   5,602   6,700   9,403
       −2,333   −3,422   −2,147

D.   8,021   7,602   6,040
       −4,262   −3,445   −4,272

More Zeros

More difficult subtraction

A. $\begin{array}{r} 9,000 \\ -2,123 \\ \hline \end{array}$ $\begin{array}{r} 7,000 \\ -2,564 \\ \hline \end{array}$ $\begin{array}{r} 6,000 \\ -3,322 \\ \hline \end{array}$ $\begin{array}{r} 4,000 \\ -1,241 \\ \hline \end{array}$

B. $\begin{array}{r} 5,000 \\ -2,602 \\ \hline \end{array}$ $\begin{array}{r} 8,000 \\ -3,405 \\ \hline \end{array}$ $\begin{array}{r} 7,000 \\ -3,629 \\ \hline \end{array}$ $\begin{array}{r} 6,000 \\ -2,351 \\ \hline \end{array}$

C. $\begin{array}{r} 5,002 \\ -1,229 \\ \hline \end{array}$ $\begin{array}{r} 5,001 \\ -3,222 \\ \hline \end{array}$ $\begin{array}{r} 8,005 \\ -3,009 \\ \hline \end{array}$ $\begin{array}{r} 9,004 \\ -3,115 \\ \hline \end{array}$

Another Challenge

A.

9,231	8,000	7,004	6,021
−6,009	−5,333	−5,209	−2,052

B.

7,304	7,103	6,000	8,240
−2,116	−3,024	−1,009	−2,000

Do you need help on this?

C.

9,002	5,000
−4,008	−2,002

D.

6,401	4,000
−3,122	−1,111

What's Left?

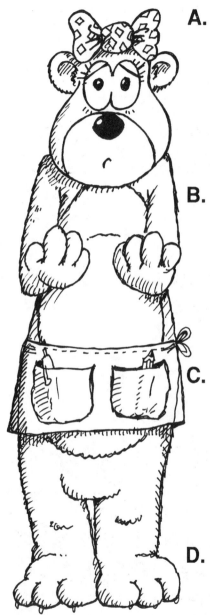

A. $20.00 $50.00 $70.00
     − 10.07   − 29.95   − 17.50

B. $30.07 $40.00 $60.05
     − 12.09   − 13.75   − 19.95

C. $80.04 $90.00 $90.50
     − 30.07   − 37.59   − 11.27

D. $60.00 $70.00 $40.00
     − 23.99   − 52.09   − 17.98

Review

A. $\begin{array}{r} 7,420 \\ -2,601 \\ \hline \end{array}$ $\begin{array}{r} 8,235 \\ -4,166 \\ \hline \end{array}$ $\begin{array}{r} 6,126 \\ -2,999 \\ \hline \end{array}$ $\begin{array}{r} 9,000 \\ -\quad\ \ 5 \\ \hline \end{array}$

B. $\begin{array}{r} 7,002 \\ -\quad 329 \\ \hline \end{array}$ $\begin{array}{r} 5,004 \\ -1,206 \\ \hline \end{array}$ $\begin{array}{r} 7,004 \\ -5,116 \\ \hline \end{array}$ $\begin{array}{r} 7,203 \\ -4,102 \\ \hline \end{array}$

C. $\begin{array}{r} 8,004 \\ -7,118 \\ \hline \end{array}$ $\begin{array}{r} 8,000 \\ -1,222 \\ \hline \end{array}$ $\begin{array}{r} 9,239 \\ -4,333 \\ \hline \end{array}$

D. $\begin{array}{r} 4,601 \\ -2,513 \\ \hline \end{array}$ $\begin{array}{r} 4,002 \\ -1,222 \\ \hline \end{array}$ $\begin{array}{r} 4,000 \\ -2,007 \\ \hline \end{array}$

Good luck.

Score: _____

Time: _____

Rewrite and Solve!

Line up the columns!

A. 4,269 – 2,147 = ? $$\begin{array}{r}4{,}269\\-2{,}147\\\hline 2{,}122\end{array}$$	**B.** 5,269 – 864 = ?
C. 9,420 – 600 = ?	**D.** 9,000 – 8 = ?	**E.** 9,243 – 1,409 =?
F. 8,420 – 99 = ?	**G.** 7,420 – 87 = ?	**H.** 7,000 – 57 = ?
I. 8,874 – 3,629 =?	**J.** 4,831 – 763 = ?	**K.** 7,315 – 48 = ?

© Frank Schaffer Publications, Inc.

FS-8159 Homework Helpers—Subtraction Grade 3

About How Much?

A. 9,002 − 4,000 = ?

○ about 5
○ about 50
○ about 500
⊗ about 5,000

B. 8,003 − 5,000 = ?

○ about 1,000
○ about 3,000
○ about 5,000
○ about 7,000

C. 9,280 − 3,005 = ?

○ about 2,000
○ about 4,000
○ about 6,000
○ about 8,000

D. 4,800 − 2,700 = ?

○ about 1,000
○ about 2,000
○ about 3,000
○ about 4,000

E. 8,605 − 8,300 = ?

○ about 1,000
○ about 2,000
○ about 3,000
○ about 4,000

F. 5,940 − 2,300 = ?

○ about 2,000
○ about 3,000
○ about 4,000
○ about 5,000

G. 8,050 − 3,030 = ?

○ about 1,000
○ about 3,000
○ about 5,000
○ about 7,000

H. 5,630 − 5,400 = ?

○ about 1,000
○ about 2,000
○ about 3,000
○ about 4,000

I. 9,250 − 1,800 = ?

○ about 1,000
○ about 3,000
○ about 5,000
○ about 7,000

J. 7,780 − 4,695 = ?

○ about 1,000
○ about 3,000
○ about 5,000
○ about 7,000

K. 6,800 − 5,320 = ?

○ about 2,000
○ about 4,000
○ about 6,000
○ about 8,000

Estimation

A. $50.00 – $4.99 ○ about $5.00 ○ about $15.00 ○ about $25.00 ○ about $45.00	**B.** $30.00 – $14.95 ○ about $5.00 ○ about $15.00 ○ about $25.00 ○ about $45.00	**C.** $40.00 – $9.95 ○ about $10.00 ○ about $20.00 ○ about $30.00 ○ about $40.00
D. $60.00 – $29.95 ○ about $10.00 ○ about $20.00 ○ about $30.00 ○ about $40.00	**E.** $90.00 – $39.98 ○ about $30.00 ○ about $50.00 ○ about $70.00 ○ about $90.00	**F.** $80.00 – $19.95 ○ about $20.00 ○ about $40.00 ○ about $60.00 ○ about $80.00
G. $70.00 – $9.99 ○ about $20.00 ○ about $40.00 ○ about $60.00 ○ about $80.00	**H.** $50.00 – $19.95 ○ about $5.00 ○ about $10.00 ○ about $20.00 ○ about $30.00	**I.** $60.00 – $4.98 ○ about $5.00 ○ about $15.00 ○ about $25.00 ○ about $55.00
J. $90.00 – $49.99 ○ about $20.00 ○ about $40.00 ○ about $60.00 ○ about $80.00	**K.** $20.00 – $14.98 ○ about $5.00 ○ about $10.00 ○ about $20.00 ○ about $30.00	**L.** $50.00 – $24.97 ○ about $5.00 ○ about $15.00 ○ about $25.00 ○ about $55.00

Review

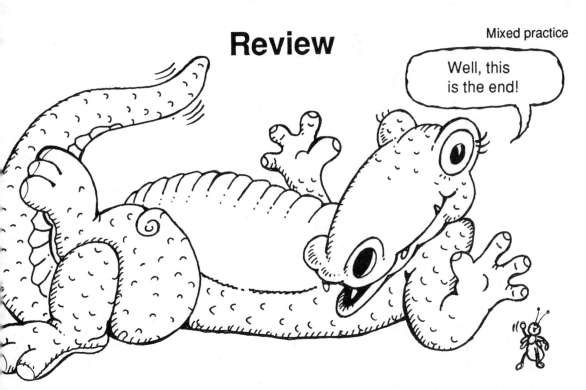

Well, this
is the end!

A. 9,400   7,000   8,123   6,497
     −   3   −   429   −7,466   −2,346

B. 6,003   8,000   5,001   7,642
     −1,002   −4,000   −   909   −3,447

C. 8,643   4,926   6,000
     −   999   −   900   −   1

Score: _____

Time: _____

© Frank Schaffer Publications, Inc.   49   FS-8159 Homework Helpers—Subtraction Grade 3

Good Work!

SUBTRACTION AWARD
presented to

_____

for successfully completing
this Homework Helpers Book

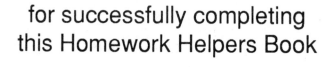

_____
signed

_____
date

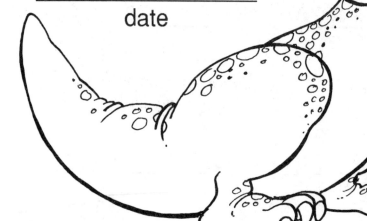

© Frank Schaffer Publications, Inc.

Help is here for the child who needs extra practice with basic skills or for the accelerated child who enjoys an extra challenge. These inexpensive, compact books boost self-confidence and reinforce skills with fun-to-do activities and appealing art that really motivates children. Look for our entire line of Homework Helpers at an Educational Supply Store near you.

See our Homework Helpers collection at a store near you.

FRANK SCHAFFER'S

Homework Helpers

Making learning fun!

CAT. NO. FS-8159
Printed in the U.S.A.
ISBN 0-86734-126-2

0 17257 08159